A COLLECTION OF MAGICAL
FAIRYTALES FOR ADULTS
AND CHILDREN ALIKE.

Middle Earth Magic
First Edition 2016
ISBN: 978-0-9934737-0-8

Published By:
www.angeluspoetry.com

DEDICATED TO:
ALL THE LOST SOULS

Special dedication to:
James, Buddy & Anna
Thank you for helping me to
remember how to find rainbows
in a world full of grey.

CONTENTS

AUTHOR'S NOTE TO ADULTS

I suppose this all started about thirty years ago, I was five years old and I had decided that I would like to be a dragon. Now in my mind I saw no problem with this, I could just be a dragon. At first, I was humoured by my parents and they went along with me being a dragon and for that time I was in my mind, a dragon. I really was you know, I was a dragon! My name was Gorbash and I could breathe fire and fly. It met with a surprised and bewildered reception at school during the name calling register.

"Gerard Thompson...
Gerard Thompson...
Gerard!"

I sat with my arms and legs folded on the hard floor with all the other children, staring intently at the teacher but not answering her. After a short delay, I then announced...

"My name is Gorbash now Miss"
"Gorbosh?"
"Gorbaaash Miss! It's my dragon name, I'm a dragon!"

"Ok Gerard"
"Gorbash!!!"
"OK Gorbosh"

The teacher rolled her eyes and then briskly moved to the next pupil who didn't want to be a dragon quite as much as I did. Not enough to speak out and proclaim it at least.

"Philip Johnson?"
"Here Miss"

As smooth as that! Philip was such a teacher's pet, he never changed his name or wanted to be a dragon. I never understood that boy I thought he was mad!

Over the weeks to come the absurdity of Gorbash actually being a real dragon was explained to Gerard by different adults until he finally gave up on the brilliant idea of being a dragon. I just got worn down by intellectual logic I guess. Over the best part of the next three decades, the wearing down continued. In the same way that rivers erode rocks, society taught me how to let go of my creative imagination and work with what was "real". Invisible friends evanesced, the tooth fairy slipped away, Father Christmas died in a mangled sleigh crash of childhood disillusion. There were no survivors, not even the Angels I once talked to of a night when everyone else was asleep. It was an all out massacre, a systematic slaying of dozen upon dozen of elves, bogeymen, monsters and superheroes of my own imaginative creation. Reflecting on it, I don't think my imagination ever really went away as I grew in years, I was just taught to use it in a more "normal" way, a more respectable adult way. I was guided to use it to envision life situations that I did not want to happen and may very well never occur. This was what the adults call worrying. All adults worry it's part of being an adult, even adults who have no worries feel obliged to worry, or the other adults may think they are somewhat peculiar.

It's such a tragedy when the magic dulls in a person, when we start to think that something can only be real if we can see it with our eyes or hold it in our hands. It took me a long time to remember what all children know. That something becomes real when you choose to believe in it, in the exact second that you feel it in your heart and believe in it with your entire soul. Anyhow, my world just kept getting greyer and greyer and the magic inside me sort of shrank and shrank until there was just an empty space inside me where it once resided.

My writing of stories began at school as a child but tapered off for some years with the onset of greyness to be reborn during a very dark time which involved my youngest son becoming critically ill. Thankfully he is now very stable and his condition manageable, however, he did have this awful habit for a while of having heart attacks and going into comas. We have since discussed this with him and he has promised both his mother and I to try his best not to do this anymore. There were many long days and nights spent at the side of a hospital bed asking for help from things I had already lost belief in, and I found that writing poetry even out of sheer helplessness, was actually in some small way cathartic. I would love to tell you that this book came from a happy place, but as this is a book of true stories (with just a smidge of artistic licence) I'll resist the temptation to lie. Although I would never have admitted it to anyone at the time, not even myself, I had become very anxious and depressed. Looking back at it, during his illness I may have had a spiritual awakening, or I may have gone quite mad. Maybe the only difference is whether you believe in angels or not. If that is true, I will call it an awakening because I now believe in angels. When I speak of angels I don't just mean as winged messengers from above. I also mean ones living among us here on earth disguised in the form of kind and loving human beings.

Following his illness and recovery, I was forced to find new ways to create joy in my life and found those joys in the spiritual, poetic and mystical realms. I was lucky enough to still have my youngest son as a teacher to help me. I began to study him and the way he looked at the world with wonder and an open mind. I don't mind admitting that I was in complete awe of him. As I watched on I made realisations, sometimes just small things like how he smiled because smiling makes you feel happy, rather than waiting for something to make you happy before you smile. His small but brilliant mind unclouded by knowledge could see the magic all around us that somewhere along the way I had lost sight of. Through studying him closely, somehow I was for short periods privileged enough to be able to view the world from a child's perspective and figured that just maybe; this could be the real world that I had somehow forgotten how to remember. What I was searching for was very hard to find at first. It hid away in the smallest and most unlikely places, in toy cars, leprechauns and childhood dreams. I found something there that I would like to share with you, the reader. I found hope, and also some of the magic that was missing from my life since I was a very young boy.

A friend once said that the furthest journey you will ever make will be only fourteen inches long, between one's head and one's heart. He also said that many people would not have the courage to travel it. This is my journey so far, in fairytales. I would like to dedicate this book to my sons James & Buddy and my Granddaughter Anna, but also to all the lost souls; past, present and future. I hope that it can maybe help a Norman get out from under a bridge, a Princess with her goblins, an Evol to get home from his castle, a little girl who made a wish or hid her teddy bear away. Perhaps, even just a reminder for somebody to water their flower. Most of all I hope the tales that got me smiling again, make you smile too.

Love

Gorbash (-;

Open the pages and climb on in,
for this is where we shall begin.

Climb into the boat and hoist the sails,
for a magical voyage of fairytales...

FOUR
LEAF
CLOVER

I saw two leprechauns last night,
doing a dance around our garden light.

So I crept out the front and down our back alley,
with my hood pulled up just like a scally.

Scaled next door's fence, then over ours,
with a fishing net and two jam jars.

Then I crept up I caught the two
they didn't know just what to do.

Believe me this is truth, not children's fable!
I placed them on our kitchen table.

They were at first quite angry, but soon chilled out,
when I told them, what my plan's about.

I said....

"I'd like to teach the world you're real,
try to change the way that people feel
See we've lost our magic, become quite lost,
don't know true wealth, always counting cost.
We live just like we'll never die,
more concerned about these things we buy.

One Leprechaun sighed, said...

"This is true!

But I'm afraid my friend, we can't help you.
You see middle earth since time began,
has always lived in tune with man.
But then man, you changed,
you became, less gentle.
Began wars and killing and all things mental,
polluted rivers, cut down trees,
brought mother nature to her knees.
So we sought shelter, hid away,
then you stopped believing one sad day.
And For Man! The greatest shame of all!
Was when you lost your faith in all things small.
You didn't just lose leprechauns, fairies and tiny elves,
you stopped believing in yourselves.
Chose fear not love became soooooo selfish,
then lost your faith in all things elfish.
But you good sir, we can't deceive,
you have shown the courage to believe.
But grant us our freedom? Please now set us free?
For this is now the way, things have to be."

And with tear in eye for Seamus and Steve,
I lifted jars so they could leave.

But they stayed and talked 'til night was over,
then handed me a four leaf clover.

I knew my new found friends I would now miss,
but before they left granted me, one wish.

Then as Seamus first had, I let out a sigh,
And wished that leprechauns would...
Never!
Ever!
Die!

BRUM

To us it's just a little car,
but to him it's like buried treasure,
The joy of digging it out the toy box
just fills his world with pleasure.
You see to big people it is just a little toy.
A truck that's red and yellow,
but when he sees it, it's like a long lost
friend that shouts...

"I'M OVER HERE MATE HEEEELLLLLOOO!

Have you come back to play with me?
Could our adventures once again begin?
Remember last time though?
That thing with the toilet!
You know that I can't swim!!!!"
His heart is alight as he picks it up
and he holds it in his hand,
he smiles at us as though explaining,
but we'll never understand.
He drives it around on hands and knees,
race track of laminate floors,
to him, this toy is a work of art,
the thing that he adores.

Circumnavigates the etch a sketch
and there's no time for dinner,
the conservatory is now a Grand Prix track
and his truck, will be the winner.

He's kitted out in his own driver's uniform
and he's looking his best.
With a make do helmet of messy hair
and a chocolate medalled vest.

It's got, painted on eyes and a smiley face
where the number plate should be,
he looks at its face and smiles right back.
He really thinks that it can see!
I watch with envy, think of my own car,
see this game of push and shove,
doesn't need diesel, tyres, servicing.
His truck just runs on love.

Then when it's time for bed tonight
he wants to bring his truck,
but trucks aren't meant for bedtime Buddy,
so son, you're out of luck.
Because trucks are hard and made of plastic
and not really safe for bed,
so with magician's skill and slight of hand,
Mum swaps for Ted instead.

Because I'm his dad, I really should know better
and you may think I'm berserk,
but when I put the truck back in its box,
whisper...

"Goodnight Brum,
good work"

PITYSELF
BRIDGE

There's a place on the trail that's as cold as a fridge,
a cramped damp dark tunnel, under Pityself bridge.

Now, Norman the troll loves to hide in that place,
with his sticky up hair and great big sad face.

He moans through the morning,
he moans through the night,
he argues with others and just wants to fight.

He gets himself angry then kicks at the wall,
and never plays out when his friends come to call.

He tells himself stories of how life is unfair,
and pushes away all of those who would care.

"No one understands me and nobody helps!"
The tunnel it echoed his cries and his yelps.

Then one day when Norman sat down on a boulder,
a tiny wood sprite took her seat on his shoulder

"Hey Norman!" she shouted,
as she yanked on his stubble.
"You know if you stay here you're really in trouble!"

So the tiny brave sprite asked for Norman to laugh,
or if he can't do this, at least take a bath!

She giggled and tickled his big hairy belly.

"Get a wash in the stream you!
You're really quite smelly!"

So Norman stood up and he trudged to the stream,
then thought of the ways that his life could have been.

The time that he spent as a big angry nark
the hours of the daylight he'd stayed in the dark.

His reflection was scary, where was the old Norman?
He was once young and handsome,
not sad, old and boring.

He remembered the day he'd stepped over a ridge,
then fell onto his bum, under Pityself bridge.

The dark there was comfy, it seemed to conceal,
his feeling of heartache and make it less real.

Like a warm snugly blanket of blackness and tears,
it felt so familiar he'd stayed there for years.
He just lost his courage when he fell onto his bum,
it seemed to confuse him and make him all numb.

He lost touch with his smiles, and then with his laughter,
made the tiniest thing out to be a disaster.

So he jumped in the stream and he had a good rinse,
then he listened to sprite as she tried to convince.

"We all sometimes trip Norm,
it's one thing worth knowing!
We all have to fall, it's for learning and growing.
Your smiles and your laughter are over that ridge,
but you'll have to be brave and leave Pityself bridge!"

Poor Norman was scared
it was all he had known,
held his head in his hands,
then let out a great...

"GRRROOOAAAN!!!!!"

He summoned the courage to head over the ridge,
then took long painful strides out of Pityself bridge.

He saw tulips and roses and white butterflies,
as the tears of his heart came to fill up his eyes.

Heard children all laughing, the sounds filled his ears,
he started to smile as he wiped off the tears.

Looked back at the tunnel, a shadow he saw,
the ghost of a troll that now lived there no more.

Though his time at the bridge, it was really quite crappy.
He had to learn to be sad, so he'd know how...
To be happy (-:

HOME
SWEET
GNOME

When the lights go out and no one's about
in the gardens of our homes,
there comes the cheery, happy shout,
of our friends the garden gnomes.

They know it's spring and work they must.
They have a lot to do!
The behind the scenes work, that goes unnoticed,
by the likes of me and you.

There's a hive of hustle bustle
from behind the garden bins,
which means... It's time for some repairs
before the new day then begins.

Who did you think glued leaves to trees
and put the batteries in hedgehogs?

Who massages the tired limbs
of the poor old jumped out pond frogs?

Every day they swap a bigger head
on those flowers that don't bloom,
they have assorted sizes stashed away
in an underground store room.

They put their backs out just stretching grass,
so the humans think it grows,
doing summersaults with perfume guns,
just in case you smell that rose.

Now gardening is a lot of work
and of gardening, they are fond,
but there's always time for skinny dips
in next door's Koi Carp pond.

And when autumn visits, no cutting corners,
they don't take leaves straight down.
They climb tree branches with little pails
and paint them gold and brown.

Paint some leaves orange, others yellow,
until their masterpiece complete.
But before they drop them down, make sure,
that they're crispy for your feet.

So the next night pop them in the toaster
to make sure they go CCRRRUUNNCH!

Then tuck the squirrels up in bed,
they're such a caring bunch.

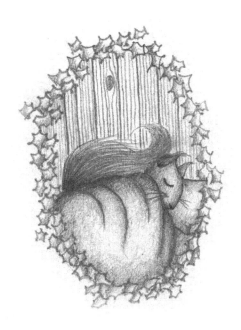

But Gnome work it fell, as the mixers turned,
and the green it turned to grey.
Mother Earth she cried as the gnome work died,
and she watched on in dismay.
And as the flags were laid the gnomes no longer played,
our parks and gardens became gnomeless.
Gnomes queued in lines at unemployment signs,
and became destitute and homeless.
And as we drove more cars and dumped more junk,
the saddest sound was heard.
A tiny cough down in the grass,
of a choking ladybird.

But...

There is always hope and it can start right here,
right here in our own homes.
Let's pull the concrete up, plant some trees
and make work..

For garden gnomes!

I BELIEVE
IN FAIRIES

I believe in fairies...
Don't tell me that you don't!

You don't believe in fairies?
Is it that you don't? Or Won't?

Yes, I believe in goblins, trolls and fairies,
and pink and yellow polka dot canaries.

I believe in wizards and dragons and magic,
and fairytales both joyful and tragic.
I can conjure them in my own mind,
see them clear although they are blind.

You may write me off as a raging nutter,
but when was the last time your heart gave,
a flutter?

With magic, wonder, innocence,
or would you prefer to just see sense?

Live in that world of black and grey?
See problems, suffering and dismay?

Yes! I believe in fairies, don't beg my pardon,
I watch them play in our back garden.

Watch with wonder, give a smile,
then go back to their world a while.

That normal world that they believe in,
so grey, so cold, devoid of feeling.

This world they believe in, is it bad?
So you'd prefer this, now who's mad?

Remember as a child the world was sweet,
and fairies danced around at your feet.

Where all imagined became real,
no time for science, reason, spiel.

You could say I chose my own delusion.
Yes I chose it, over life's confusion.

That black magic that keeps adults bound,
I shrugged it off and fairies found.

You see...

Fairies aren't just real within my mind,
they dance where hearts are warm and actions kind.

Well if you don't believe,
then let your fairies die,

but if the kids can see them...

So!
Can!
I!

MACABRE
CASTLE

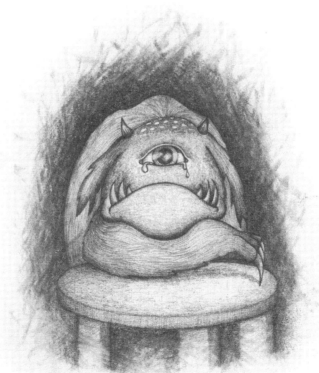

The Macabre castle
stood on the hill
long since forgotten,
as though time stood still.
Open your mind's eye
and picture this scene
a castle so scary
no child's ever been.
The sun does not set
on its great grey cold walls
and even the battlements look lonely
in the rain as it falls.

And the drawbridge resembles
the teeth of a shark,
as its broken wood splinters
stick out in the dark.
In the past king's old throne room,
dwells a solitary beast
he sits alone at a table
where once they did feast.
He bangs and he howls
the most terrible screams
those noises they echo the walls
like bad dreams.
And no person comes near,
for they all are too scared
of the stories and whispers and rumours they've heard.

Of the beast, they call Evol
who dwells in that place
although they've all heard the stories,
no one's yet seen his face.

Some say...
"He breathes fire and has teeth made of iron!"
Some say...
"He has wings and they've seen Evol flying!"
Some say...
"He eats dormice and rats, slugs and snails!"
Some say...
"He fires arrows from his long fingernails!"
Some say...
"He is purple!"
Some say...
"He is black"
Some say...
"He has one eye and a hump on his back!!!!!"

The stories all change
but one thing stays the same,
they say that Evol the beast
he is crazy, insane.

But then one day,
a good boy with heart true and kind
stumbled up to the castle,
he was lost and was blind.
Made his way across the drawbridge

and into the courtyard,
then he followed the sound
of someone crying so hard.
So he followed the sound
of a cry and a yelp
true of those pure of heart
he just wanted to help.
As he felt through the tunnels
the sounds they got clearer,
and his heart filled with sadness,
as the boy he got nearer.

He asked himself...

"Who could this person be?
Why is he so sad?
Why does he stay here alone
in this place cold and bad?"

Well, when he entered the throne room
and caught Evol's sight,
it wasn't the boy who got scared,
but the beast got a fright!

No person had come here
for so many years,
he had sat here alone
with his pain and his tears.
He had sat here so lonesome
in the cold, wind and rain,

now this poor little blind boy
had braved his domain.
Evol was surprised
as this boy slight and thin
felt his way to the table
and sat next to him.

"DONT YOU KNOW
I'M A MONSTEEEEERRR!!!!!!!"

Evol screamed at the lad.

"I don't hear a monster,
I just hear someone who's sad."

Then the boy he reached out
and he held the beast's hands
and the beast was so glad
that someone understands.
Then something strange happened,
that had not for a while.
The Beast, he felt love,
and this made Evol smile.

So they made friends and chatted,
this boy wanted to hear
how a nice beast like Evol
had come to live here?
Then Evol he told him
a tale very sad

of how Evol looked different.
He was once treated bad.
Other Monsters had teased him
and this broke Evol's heart,
said he was ugly and stupid,
said he wasn't too smart.

You see...

This teasing hurts more
than a cut or a graze
it can be ten times more painful
and in so many ways.
And when Evol got hurt,
didn't know what to do
because he thought what they said
was so real and so true.

Then as they chatted further
poor old Evol explained
how he hid here one day
in the dark as it rained.
And the clouds never lifted
and the sun never shone
and how he thought
no one would miss him
or realise that he'd gone.

Then the boy hugged him tight and said,

"Evol you fool!
Don't you know it's just the bad kids
that tease you at school?"

Evol was so glad
when he heard this boy's truth
that he jumped up so high
that his head whacked the roof.
He was happy and dancing
because he knew this was right
and they stayed up and laughed
and told jokes through the night.
Then when morning came,
a surprise it did bring:
the sun shone on the castle
and the birds they did sing.
Then the flowers they opened
and the grass it did grow
and the boy convinced Evol
it was time he should go.
Go home to his family,
who he'd missed very much.
So great were the effects
of a kind hearted touch
that Evol agreed
and he left with a smile
and said goodbye to that castle
where he'd lived for a while,
then ran home to his family,
who were filled with such joy.

You see he was never a monster,
just a scared little boy.
He had things all backwards
and just needed a shove.
And when you spell Evol backwards
you'll see it spells...

HER &
BEAR

There was once a girl with a teddy bear,
that teddy bear was part of her.
They played, they cuddled, they'd have such fun,
they'd sing and dance and laugh and run.
And then one day, she met a boy
who wished to take care of her toy.
She loved that boy with all her heart,
she always thought they'd never part.
The boy was mean, he hurt the bear,
kicked it around, pulled out its fur.
The girl so hurt she cried and cried,
She almost thought her bear had died.
She took it home and nursed it well
her little bear had been to hell.
She swore that day no other boy
would ever do that to her toy.
She boxed bear up, hid bear away,
now her and bear no longer play.
On some sad days her heart grew soft,
she'd hear bear call down from the loft.
But out of fear she'd drown voice out
no matter how loud bear would shout.
And boys would come and boys would go
but her little bear she'd never show.

You see...

There is a bear within us all,
a tiny part that's very small.
And if she's brave, maybe some day
she'll let that bear come out to play.
Not for a boy, but for her and bear
to let bear know, she can still care.
They'll play, they'll cuddle, they'll have such fun
they'll sing and dance and laugh and run.
She will watch out for naughty boys
who come to try and hurt her toys.
But she won't be scared, afraid to feel
because bear and her
learnt how to heal.

THE LITTLE FLOWER BOY

A little boy he found a seed
that may become his flower.
He took it home to keep it safe
within an ivory tower.

He placed it on a window ledge
in bedding made of soil.
He gave it food and sheltered it
so sunlight would not spoil.

He watered it and soon enough,
so strongly there it stood.
His hopeful heart began to swell
when slowly, formed one bud.

The vision of that flower he'd seen
within that seed so small.
Was happening before his eyes
as stem became so tall.

Then as that flower opened
he watched on in sheer delight.
He tended to her every day,
stared at her late at night.

Their spirits touched as if as one,
for the first time he felt whole.
That little seed he'd nurtured,
had now somehow, touched his soul.

But as the boy grew older
he then lessened his concern,
important work became his life
so flower waited turn.

He watered her just now and then
and sometimes he forgot.
Just kept her there upon a ledge,
within a tiny pot.

Too important now to notice
and too busy to feel guilt.
No longer could that flower grow
and slowly she did wilt.

Poor flower longed so for the day
her boy would notice her.
But even when he was around
he wasn't really there.

The importance of the world outside
had blinded him to beauty.
So even when he tended her
such acts were born of duty.

So yes there are important things
outside our ivory towers.
But there's no job more important
than to take care of our flowers.

So boys forget
and sometimes flowers too,
that love is not a duty.
Another thing gets lost then too;
we fail to see true beauty.

So if you have a flower
then please see it with new eyes.
Be true to it, protect it
and don't ever tell it lies.

Let it know that it's important,
let such caring bring you joy.

Maybe that day, a man may flower
from a little boy.

THE PRINCESS OF MAPLELEAF

In Mapleleaf a princess lived,
more beautiful than spring,
but her beauty came at a great cost
and sadness it did bring.
When only young a magic curse
was placed upon her crown,
that goblins whisper in her ears
and make her feel so down.
See goblins they are horrid things
that whisper through the night,
they say that you aren't worthy
and then steal away your light.
As beautiful as the princess was
she did not know her worth,
so she wandered nature taking solace
from the Mother Earth.
Princes they came and said they loved
but she never did believe,
because what they said they saw in her
she never could conceive.
They whispered kind words in her ear;
they wanted her so bad,
but somehow goblin voices shouted louder!
Sent her mad.
Once in a while, she'd trust a prince
to catch her when she falls,
but when she really needed them
they missed her gentle calls.
See princes, they are funny things
who take and then depart,

so she longed to meet a prince who saw
the colours of her heart.
Those goblins they made fun of this
and chattered in her ears,
so she stayed lonely wondering for
ohhhh so many years.
Then one day, she made a choice
to not wait on a prince,
those goblins they went quieter
and have been ever since.
No one to love or try to please
all princes placed on shelf,
our princess made a choice that day
to learn to love herself.
See, we all have goblins in our heads
that come to steal our light,
to tell us we're not good enough
as we lay there late at night.
And no spell can drive out goblins,
they will always be not far,
but their whispers cannot hurt us
when we love just who we are.
So sometimes we have to wonder
and take solace from the earth,
to realise we can't look outside,
to find out what we're worth.
All people they are different,
so diverse and so unique,
but if we seek our worth outside
we always become weak.

Though those we love can give us strength,
such strength it starts within,
we must all know where their love ends
and our love does begin.
One Fateful day she met a man,
but a poet not a prince,
he knew this princess loved herself,
saw no need to convince.
He saw the goblins in her head,
he knew those goblins well,
he'd one day learnt to love himself
and also break their spell.
He saw the colours in her heart
and matched them with his own,
he saw a rainbow in her soul
like he had never known.
Then a funny thing did happen
when she finally stopped her trying,
those tears of pain she'd wept for years
turned into joyful crying.
As no man had tried to fix her
or convince her that she's good,
these things she had done on her own,
this man just understood.
In his arms she fell, and their hearts did touch,
and she held on very tight,
then for the first time in her life she knew,
she was safe through the night.

A LITTLE GIRL'S WISH

A little girl she made a wish
to one day know, true love,
she closed her eyes and whispered words
to Angels up above.

Her Angels were quite cautious
as they always do know best,
but true to her they waved their wings
and granted her request.

A boy was sent with an open heart
and quickly they did fall,
he cared for her, treated her well,
and each night he would call.

For hours they would chat in bed,
of love and life and fun,
the girl knew love for her first time,
their tale had now begun.

So all seemed perfect for a while,
all love and trust and highs,
but the little girl she made mistakes
and told some tiny lies.

The boy was hurt, he loved her so,
but he'd known lies before,
he knew one lie could lead to two
and maybe thousands more.

So though his heart was true to her,
his head it told him no,
because lies a love had told before
had made him feel so low.

Their Angels watched on from above
as both their hearts did break,
as damage done takes long to heal,
eyes water, hands do shake.

See love is truth and lies are fear
and with fear pain does come,
hearts that once did swell with love
then shrink and start to numb.

The truth; it does move slowly
but it always finds its way,
those lies you whisper in the night
will one day know the day.

So her Angels showed her love at last,
and true love that was real,
then showed her pain and heartache too
and just how that can feel.

But Angels are not careless
and this tale it leads to more,
see broken hearts
when mended then...

love better than before.

THE
MAGICIAN OF
ASPIREVILLE

nce, not so long ago, there was a great kingdom called "The Kingdom of Aspireville". Now, Aspireville was one of those places where it seemed as though there was a great need for everybody to always, always look their best. To be looking young and beautiful was very important to the people who lived there and growing old almost seemed like a sin in the eyes of many. People of the kingdom often cursed their bodies if they were seemingly too round or too wrinkly or even too old. It seemed as though they were cursing themselves, but it is in all of our natures to grow old and wrinkly, and sometimes a little rounder than what we should be. The fact is, they were actually cursing Mother Nature herself.

Along the great boulevard of Aspireville were many, many boutiques and emporiums. Some carried the latest expensive fashions and salubrious jewels. Some sold magic boxes with flat crystal screens, which its citizens could glare into and be magically hypnotised. Upon the screens of those magic boxes, the faces of all the most beautiful and famous people in the whole of Aspireville would appear and talk to anyone who owned one. The most beautiful and famous would tell all of the city's people who wanted to be just like them, exactly what else they needed to purchase to, supposedly, become the happiest they had ever been.

The grandest of all of the emporiums on the boulevard was the 'Magicians Boutique'. The Magician of Aspireville had once been a great healer who had helped the sick of the town. He one day began to look at how its people felt so sad when they grew wrinkly, old or a little too round. He decided with the best intentions in the world that he would dedicate his life to helping these people. He wanted to develop a new system of magic that would make people feel better about how they looked.

To achieve this, the Magician had travelled many miles through many countries to consult the greatest magic practitioner in the entire world for help, The Grand Sorcerer. This Grand Sorcerer knew of all types of magic and after a brief chat with the magician, walked to his study and lifted an old book of magic from his bookshelves. He held it aloft, and then proceeded to blow the layers of dust from it revealing the title, 'The Book of Lines'. The Magician was then given the magic book of lines to study along with the thinnest wand he had ever seen, a wand as thin as a needle. The Grand Sorcerer gave that book to the Magician on one condition only, that he would one day return it when he had learnt all that this book had to teach him. He told the Magician that on that day, he would be ready to become a Sorcerer himself and learn of the truest of all magic available to help mankind.

When the Magician returned to Aspireville, he went straight to work. He found that he could wave his needle-thin wand over a person's face and take away any facial lines they did not want, and even add new ones to change the shape of their face. Business became so busy that he had to take on a lady as a helper to keep up with the workload. She was a good hard working girl with children; she was never late and always did her best. In the years that came to pass, the Magician became extremely rich and his business grew and grew as the people of Aspirville became more and more dependent on his work. One day on an unusually slow evening the Magician and his helper were sat together chatting and he noticed some tiny lines in the corner of the girl's eyes. He asked if she would like them removed? The girl smiled sweetly, then gracefully thanked him, but said that she would not like that. The Magician thought that she may just have been being her usual polite self in refusing. He told her that there would be no charge to her for this magic and that actually, he would really love to do this for her as a small reward for her years of dutiful service and friendship. The girl again politely declined his offer. The Magician could not understand why. He couldn't help but wonder why, if almost every other girl in the kingdom would gladly pay a month's wages for his magic, this girl, who was in comparison very poor, would not accept his services for free.

The girl then explained how the other girls who came to see him may not have met their true love yet. She told him that before she had met her true love she would have liked to have had her lines worked on, but not now. She explained how she had always been insecure and wanted to change the way that she looked until she met a man one day. This man wasn't perfect at all, in many people's eyes, he would not have been seen as the most attractive or handsome man. She had however seen something in him, something that maybe nobody else in the world could see that made all his imperfections more perfect than any line that could be drawn by a Wizard's hand. To her, he was the most perfect man alive, as she loved him with all of her heart. He loved her the same way also. Of a night, he would stare into her eyes and trace the outline of her face with his fingertips, so gently that they almost didn't touch her. He would follow each line, each dimple and each freckle. He would run his hands over her messy hair, and then pull her head into his chest so she could fall asleep listening to his heartbeat in her ear. The ears that she always thought were a little too pointy in fact. He said he liked her ears because she looked a little like the fairies that lived in the forest and this made her glow inside.

The magician asked her why she did not feel self-conscious with somebody studying her imperfections so closely and intimately. The girl admitted that at first she had, but then her true love had told her something one night that made her understand that she did not have to be self-conscious anymore. Although it did take all of her bravery to believe in his loving and true words, and she probably would never have if she did not feel exactly the same way about him. He told her that her face to him was like a map that he liked to study and that each line was like a road. Upon that map lay sign posts and they signified every time she had cried, every time she had laughed, every tear, every smile, every boy that had broken her heart and every time she had comforted a crying child in her arms until sunrise. He told her it was this map that had led her to find him. He asked her never to change that map to be like the other girls who saw the Magician at her work. He also told her that he was worried that if she ever became lost again, like they both were before they found each other, she may never find her way back to him if that map had changed. Although this was maybe silly of him, she understood how much she would hate it if the Magician was to change even the tiniest detail of her true loves features. She agreed never to change herself if he would promise the same.

She then looked at the situation if it were the other way around. She had heard people telling tales of backstreet Magicians offering potions to make men more muscular. Even offering silver packets of strange blue triangle shaped herbs that would strengthen a man's lance for jousting. She perished the thought of him ever seeing one of these Magicians, as she was already completely contented by him. To her he was perfect in every way and she could not stand the thought of him ever feeling insecure in himself enough to seek their help. She then agreed to try to view herself through the loving eyes that he viewed her through, and despite all of her insecurities totally accept that she was all he needed too. This became their lovers pact and there was no way that she was prepared to break a promise to the man she loved most in the world.

The girl then asked the Magician a question...

"Sir, if you were to take that needle wand and change the lines on my face, would you not rob my true love of admiring the journey I travelled to find him?

The Magician's eyes filled up with the most wonderful tears he had ever known, although unfortunately, his face could not move to show the emotion he felt. (Due to too much self-practice with his wand!) With not being able to read his emotions through his face very well, the girl asked why his eyes had filled with tears? His reply came slowly through a choked and shaky voice.

"I know that your words are true, as when you held the image of your true love in your mind's eye, all of your lines disappeared. Your face became more soft and radiant than any girl I have ever seen in this whole kingdom. I know now that you know of true magic and I only know of tricks."

The Magician returned the book of lines and his needle-shaped wand to the Grand Sorcerer soon after this. He explained to the Grand Sorcerer that he now understood that the only true magic that could really help mankind; came from love, kindness and acceptance of people, as they are.

THE CITY
OF WISHES

here was once a little boy named Buddy. Buddy was a good boy, he loved his Mummy and Daddy very, very much and nearly, nearly always behaved himself. When Buddy was a little tiny baby he was very ill. The doctors said that he may not survive which made his Mummy and Daddy very sad, but they always knew deep down that Buddy would be fine no matter how ill he got or what the doctors said. You see Buddy, although very tiny, was very brave and strong. Also, Buddy had an Angel Fairy Godmother who protected him. When Buddy was very ill one night in the hospital his Angel Fairy Godmother came to see him and she told him something that nobody else could hear.

She said...

"Little baby Buddy, you are going to be very ill for a while, but you will get better and if you stay brave and strong for your Mummy and Daddy, when you are a little older, I will let you come with me to the City of Wishes and you may stay there for as long as you desire."

The Angel fairy Godmother went on to explain that in the magical City of Wishes, each morning at nine o'clock you are allowed to make one wish which will come true and stay true until the moment you fall to sleep. Then when the sun dawns again in the morning you may wish again at nine. You can be anything you like in this City. You can be a giant, a monster, a wolf, a dragon that breathes fire;

you could even choose to have superhero powers. Buddy thought that he liked his Angel Fairy Godmother, she had sparkly pretty eyes like Mummy and smelt like that smell that you only get once a year on Christmas morning when you are unwrapping your toys. That was Buddy's favourite smell!

Buddy told the Angel fairy Godmother that he was worried that his Mummy and Daddy would miss him if he visited for too long. She smiled sweetly and explained to him that he did not have to worry as one day in the City of Wishes only seemed like one second in Mummy and Daddy's world. So even if he stayed for a whole year or more he would be gone from Mummy and Daddy for less than five minutes. With his concerns put at ease, Buddy agreed to this and true to his word throughout all the time he was ill, he was the bravest strongest little boy in all of Alder Hey Children's Hospital. Sometimes he would watch his Mummy and Daddy by his hospital bed so worried and upset; by that time he had tubes sticking out of him and machines attached to him. But even though he was very poorly and felt really bad, he would always manage to smile at Mummy and Daddy so they would know he was going to be just fine. He was so brave even when they were not.

After a long time in Hospital Buddy started to feel a little better and his Mummy and Daddy were allowed to take him home. His Mummy worked very hard teaching him to eat, talk and walk again which was very difficult because he had forgotten how to do all those things while he had been ill for so long. However because she loved him so very, very much she never stopped trying. Daddy had to go back to work to earn money; he said it was because he had to pay someone called Bill. He didn't like Bill very much and said he was sick of Bills whenever the postman came. Buddy wondered if the postman was called Bill. Daddy made up for this when he came home from work because he gave the best bath times, bedtime stories and second best cuggle buggles in the whole wide world. This worked in getting Buddy better, because as everybody knows the best way to make people who have been really ill feel better is to love them with all of your heart and give them lots of cuggles too! Mummy was better than Daddy at cuggles but Daddy had stronger shoulders for sitting on.

Of a weekend Daddy would walk him everywhere on his shoulders and Buddy would imagine that he was a being a giant in the City of Wishes and then excitedly start to wonder exactly when his Angel Fairy Godmother would return to take him there to visit. Even though he was very much behind other children because he had been ill, with so much love surrounding him he soon got better and in a very short space of time it was almost like he had never been ill at all.

Then one night as Buddy was in his bed getting ready to fall asleep, a blue and white light appeared over his bed and his Angel fairy Godmother magically flew out of that light and stood over him where he lay. She explained that as he had been so brave while he was ill, it was now time for him to travel to the City of Wishes with her. Buddy liked any excuse not to go to bed on time and would much rather stay up and play any night of the week, but this night, the thought of finally going to the City of wishes made him smile so hard that the sides of his mouth actually touched his ears, nearly. He threw off his blankets and jumped up and down on his bed with delight. He clutched his Angel Fairy Godmother's hand and with a click of her heels and a wave of her wand they both flew into the blue and white light towards the City of Wishes.

He arrived in the city at exactly ten minutes to nine o'clock in the morning, which was exactly nine minutes and fifty-nine seconds longer than he needed to decide what he was going to wish to be. A train driver! He was thinking to himself that his Daddy would be very proud of him for choosing his job so quickly, as he had heard Daddy say many times that he himself still did not know what he wanted to be when he grew up. Buddy didn't really know exactly what that meant, but Daddy always giggled when he said it. Buddy spent the whole day driving his train, he picked up carriages, stopped at stations and even shovelled coal into the fire of the engine. He fell asleep that night in the seat of his train covered in coal dust and had chocolate toast stains all over his train driver's uniform and hat. He had had the best day ever and had eaten chocolate toast for breakfast dinner and tea, because obviously, in the City of Wishes you may also wish to eat whatever you like at any time of day, and chocolate toast was his most favourite of all.

When he awoke the next morning he wished to be a helicopter pilot, the next day a fearsome Pirate Captain, then he grew wings and flew, then he had X-ray vision, then he was an eagle and the day after that he was a unicorn that could run at the speed of sound. He was almost running out of ideas after the first week, but always just managed to think of something before nine o'clock. One morning he was sitting on his throne in his magnificent castle being a mighty king, and just by chance, through the window, he caught sight of another little boy that he thought he recognised sitting quietly outside the castle grounds under a tree. He took off his heavy gold crown and started to make the long walk over to the boy, after ordering his servants and subjects to wait for him in the castle. As he got closer he knew for sure it was his older brother James. James was a few years older than him and Buddy admired him very much and wanted to be just like him when he was bigger. He started to run and shouted.

"James, James it's me!"

James looked so happy to see him that he smiled so much that the sides of his mouth actually touched his ears, nearly. Buddy ran up to James and give him the biggest cuggle buggles ever, even bigger than when Mummy and Daddy do it. He had missed his brother James. Then they both sat down under the tree.

"I didn't know you were here" said James

"I didn't know you were here also" said Buddy

"Is that your kingdom, it's very nice, it's good to be king isn't it?" asked James

Buddy said yes, he then told James excitedly all about how he was King today and also started to tell James of some of the other adventures he had experienced in the City of Wishes. Then Buddy stopped talking, he had noticed something about James, he had noticed something very, very peculiar. He had noticed that his brother James did not have wings and wasn't driving a train and for that matter wasn't doing anything extraordinary at all! He wondered why this was and asked James what he had wished to be that morning.

James sighed and smiled; he then told Buddy how he had been in the City for a long time now and just yesterday he had decided to travel home. Today he had made a very different type of wish altogether. Buddy was flabbergasted! He couldn't understand why anybody, anybody in the world, would want to go home and asked James why. James was thoughtful in his response. He then explained to Buddy why he had decided to go home. He explained that he had tried all of the things Buddy had and more day after day, week after week and had also had lots of fun doing so. James had also been a train driver, a pirate as well as a monster, a cyclist winning the Tour De France, he had even been a dolphin! Buddy seemed a little bit put out that he had not already thought of being a dolphin as if he had thought of being a dolphin, he surely would have done this before being a king, as it seemed a much better idea now. Buddy quickly then consoled himself with the thought that he would wish to be a dolphin tomorrow. James went on to explain some of the reasons why he had grown a little tired of life in The City of Wishes.

Like when he was a giant, he wanted to be the biggest giant, but the next day some other boy would wish to be bigger than him, so then he would be unhappy until the following day when he could be bigger than the other boy. The same thing happened with being the best cyclist and being the fastest flyer or the dragon that could breathe the most fire. This went on for some time with James being unhappy half of the time until he realised that someone would always want to be bigger, faster or want to beat him. He only then had had enough of being miserable half of the time to realise that life in the City of Wishes wasn't half so much fun if you were competing with others. He said it was more fun if you just did your own thing and did not worry about other people, what they thought of you, or whether you could beat them at something. He went on to tell Buddy that when he wished to be the most handsome man in the City, this was no good either as even though all of the girls would want to kiss him, they were not chasing him, only the person that he had wished to be, and he would never really know who loved him for who he was. You see in the City of Wishes your handsomeness fades very quickly and all the people who once wanted you just for what you look like or for what you can do for them will lose interest in you very quickly. When this happens you can be left feeling very sad, James said.

James also told Buddy of the day when he wished to be the cleverest, this was "The worst day of all!" he exclaimed. He admitted that in one way it did made him feel good and cleverer than others when he could answer complicated questions or win arguments, but it never really made him happy and people started not liking him. But the biggest reason that it was the worst day was because he then thought too much. Buddy wondered how you can think too much, he thought that 'thinking' was a good thing to do as grownups do it a lot. In fact grownups always seemed to be telling children to think more and even how to think! James explained why it was silly, he told Buddy that if you think too much you create problems that would not exist if you hadn't thought about them. Buddy was very surprised by this but felt he understood it a little now.

He then told Buddy that yesterday for the first time he had wished to be the wisest child in the City of Wishes, and it was on that day that he had decided to return home to the real world. Buddy asked him what it was like to be the wisest and why it had made him decide to go home. James stopped and picked his nose for a few seconds and then wiped the green, gooey stuff on his t-shirt, then noticed Buddy was watching him and quickly started talking again. He told him that being wise and being clever are two very different things. James said that his day being wise was by far the best day he had spent in the City. Buddy asked why this was, James explained, he told Buddy that when you are wise you don't have to look clever or seem to know all the answers because it's just fine not to know. You realise that no one does, you are not supposed to and you never will. Wise people realise that not even the cleverest person will know all the answers. Some will pretend or even believe they do, but these are the least clever people of all, they are "Stupider than monkeys" James said and should be felt very sorry for. As they can make themselves very unhappy just by thinking all wrong. When you are wise you have the ability to let go of what you don't know and not upset yourself because you do not know it. James said that it was funny because sometimes when you stop thinking, the best answers usually come to you like magic. Buddy asked why this was and James said he didn't know and hadn't thought about it, then went back to picking his nose a little. Buddy did the same and thought that it was a good job that there were no Mummies or Daddies in the City of Wishes to tell them off for nose-picking. Then Buddy made the most of the fact that no adults could see him, and ate a huge green bogey.

After a few more minutes of brotherly nose-picking and a little bit of not talking, James started speaking again.

He told Buddy that when you are wise you realise that life isn't a competition or a race. He said we all run our own personal race with ourselves and the best you can ever do is try your best with the tools you have been gifted with. When you are wise you see very clearly that this will always be enough and even if things don't turn out exactly how you would have wished them to in your life, they will have turned out the way that they were meant to be. There is also no good reason to look at other people and what they have, or who they are too closely, as this can very quickly make you sad. The wise know it is far better to merely look closely at all the things you do have and be thankful for them, this in itself will make you happier. James said that everybody has something to be thankful for if they choose to look hard enough, even if at first they don't think they do. So it was not too hard for anyone to try this and to become a little happier.

But the most important thing that James said he found out when he was the wisest child in the City of Wishes, and that really stuck in Buddy's mind when James said it to him was this...

"In a world where everybody is trying to be someone or something that they are not, the only truly extraordinary people are those who are happy to be just who they are."

When James said this Buddy understood and said that he would follow James home tomorrow. He had one last wish to make in the morning though before he went home and had to figure out what it would be. He thought hard that night in the castle and stayed up very late pondering on his throne with his golden crown on. Then he remembered what James had told him, took off his crown and stopped thinking, he then drifted off into a wonderful peaceful sleep. Sure enough, the next morning the answer was there right at the front of his mind when he awoke. He quickly called for his Angel Fairy Godmother and she appeared straight away. He asked if he could have one last wish before he returned home, she smiled as if she already knew what he was going to wish for.

Buddy wished that for the rest of that day, everybody he loved, Mummy, Daddy, James, Grandparents, Aunties, Uncles, Cousins, baby Anna, Velveteen his rabbit and also his Angel Fairy Godmother would be Happy.

Buddy returned to his bed holding the hand of his Angel Fairy Godmother on the same night that he had left the real world, in fact, less than one minute had passed in real time. He was the happiest he had ever, ever, been. Happier than when he was driving trains or helicopters or even when he had wings or was the King. He wasn't even bothered about not wishing to be a dolphin before he came home. His Angel Fairy Godmother was so proud of him and gave him the biggest squishiest cuggle buggle ever before putting him back to bed. She then gently sprinkled some Angel Fairy dust on his head and kissed him goodnight before smiling a beautiful Angel Fairy Godmother smile. She was so proud of Buddy, not just because he had been brave when he was ill. More now for another reason, because both James and Buddy had learned the most valuable lesson they could have ever learnt before returning home from the City of Wishes. They had both made the same wish upon returning home. They had both learned that sometimes, not all the time, but sometimes the best ever type of happiness can come from not just wishing for things for yourself, but rather from just wishing to make the people you love happy.

Buddy and James drifted off to sleep that night smiling so much that the sides of their mouths actually touched their ears, nearly. (-:

FIELDS OF GOLD

any, many years ago there was a beautiful princess who was in love with a handsome prince. Although he was very handsome he was a bit of an idiot sometimes (as most young men are). Rather than stay at home in the kingdom with her, he went out fighting in a war.

Unfortunately, he managed to get himself killed and had to go and live in heaven for a while where he couldn't see the princess. When the princess was told of his passing she was standing in a field full of green. Upon hearing the news her heart broke in two and she fell to the floor lifeless.

The sun was watching from above and began to weep; now whenever tears and sunshine combine it creates a rainbow, which is always a sign that there is hope.

The sun travelled down to the princess and kissed her on the cheek, at which point the whole of the field turned a beautiful golden yellow and the princess began to breathe again. The sun whispered to her that "Love does not die with a person it is always here inside you and you must now move forward". From that day onward; a field on the earth would turn a beautiful golden yellow every time a broken heart was mended, as a message from the sun that there would always be hope of loving again.

So, as long as there are golden yellow fields and rainbows, life will always call us to move forward. No matter how bad things seem.

EPILOGUE

ANNA AND THE TREE OF LIFE

n the days before time began, the Gods just for their own amusement sent a bolt of magical lightning to the dark, barren earth. When it struck the earth there was an almighty eruption of thunder and every mountain shook, every river overflowed and every sea became stormy. The very next day the sun star drew closer to the earth; its rays lit up the earth's surface and on the exact spot where that lightning had struck stood a single tree. The tree of life as it is known to us now. That tree every day bore a different seed and every day, that seed would drop to the ground and upon touching the soil beneath gift the earth's surface with another form of life.

And so it began as the first trees, shrubs and plants took their place rooting, flowering and enriching the earth's soil. Then the eagles, wrens, robins and birds of all colours, shapes and descriptions took to the skies and encircled the earth in their majesty, gliding and bringing song and sound to the silence. Sometime later the tree bore other seed and so it came to pass that the land animals such as the horses, giraffes and elephants entered into being and took their place on the earth to live in harmony with the landscape. After that, a great river cut its path through the mountains and close to our tree and as it did the tree gifted its seeds into its overflowing powerful currents. As each seed hit the river bed the creatures of the water were brought into being. Fish, whales and dolphins followed the rivers downstream and upstream to the seas and waterfalls in the mountains of the lands and took their place in aquatic serenity with existence.

Now at this point, the tree had gifted life to three of the elements: earth, wind and water but had no way of gifting the fourth because the fourth element, being fire may damage its branches. So the very last seed it dropped to the ground of earth's outer surface was the seed of mankind. You see 'man' was the only creature which possessed the gifts of foresight and intellect, enabling mankind the ability to create and harness fire. From that day forth life as we know it began, the tree of life had gifted promise to all the four elements of the earth's outer realms and its role on the upper earth was then fulfilled. The Gods then hid the tree away in another dimension far down beneath the hills of Knoydart. Deep down beneath the ground the tree was hidden at the centre of its own sacred forest in the middle of the earth where it could then be safe for all time. Once safe in this secret garden, the tree dropped other seeds and so, just as it was on upper earth other forms of life came into being in this middle earth. Fairies, leprechauns, gnomes, trolls, hobbits, sprites and other forest-dwelling beings came first to tend the forest and the tree. Soon after this came the unicorns to bring magic to the forest and ensure that all things lived in harmony within the middle earth. Finally, the dragon's seed was dropped and the mighty dragons came powerfully forth into being. Their duty was to guard the secret entrance portal to the forest from any evil that may try to enter.

Now all was good with all in nature apart from mankind, the gift of intellect to mankind had become a curse because with mankind's intellect came pride, cunning and anger. Because of this men had become very destructive. The men and women of the earth became so proud and full of themselves that they began to hurt not only each other but also the trees, animals, fish and birds. The Gods in disgust called a meeting and the majority of them decided that mankind should be removed from the earth and cast down into the darkness of lower earth for the protection of all other life on the planet. There was one though that did not want mankind cast down into the darkness, and that was Anna the Goddess of love, who felt compassion for mankind in seeing its destructive and miserable existence in what could otherwise be a paradise. As the Goddess of love, she explained to the other Gods that it was not the fault of mankind that they had become so destructive. It was their intellect that had made them so, and to her compassionate eyes, mankind was but like children who had been gifted a toy that they did not know how to use rightly. She somehow managed to convince the other Gods that there could possibly be hope for mankind. The gift of intellect which their tree had produced in men to help gift fire to the earth had become mankind's curse, she claimed that it was only fair that they should try to find some way to put it right and give mankind another chance to live in harmony with nature and to find peace in their own souls.

The other Gods agreed with Anna's wisdom but still thought that mankind could not find its way to peace and harmony alone. Anna asked for a thousand earth years to contemplate a way to help mankind and for a thousand years the upper earth realm of men was in turmoil and destruction while she contemplated. When that thousand years had passed Anna met with all of the other Gods with a plan to put things right, but she would need all of their combined help to succeed. She asked them to bestow all of their magic, power and wisdom into her being for the time it took the earth to rotate on its axis just once. The other Gods trusting her agreed, and within that day she collected the brightest stars from the four corners of the universe, north, south, east and west. She held them in her hands above the earth and as she did they burnt her hands so fiercely that tears of pain fell from her eyes upon them, causing the stars to form into diamond-like crystals. The other Gods watched on in awe and amazement as these were the first tears to fall in the whole of the universe.

Anna rubbed her hands together crushing the crystallised stars into dust and then blew that dust with her loving Goddess breath towards the earth. That day every man woman and child on earth was gifted a guide and guardian in the form of an Angel, as messengers of unconditional love and peace to help them move towards harmony with the earth, its creatures and each other. And because Angels are made of Goddess tears and star dust, mankind would always be assured that their angels would know to draw closer to them, whenever tears would fall from a human eye.

The End (for now) XXX

(WRITTEN FOR **ANNA ELIZABETH THOMPSON** BORN: 10/12/15)

ACKNOWLEDGEMENTS

Thanks to...

I would like to thank poetry event organisers **Christopher Coey**, **Natalie Wharton** and the late **Glenys Feeney** for their kind encouragement and belief in my writing. In life, some people leave a forever fingerprint on your heart. Glenys was one of those people for me.

Mrs Hall, my teacher when I was about 8 who told me I was good at writing stories, I still remember you saying that. I'm sorry it has taken me so long to finish those stories for homework; I got there in the end.

Emlyn Jones for always coming to see me perform (even when nobody else did!)

George Milford Eleady-Cole for your continued artistic support

Paul Neads for the kind publishing advice.

Mum, **Dad**, **Lesley Bennett** &
Catherine Geogheghan-Breen for the proof reading.

Katie Wrigley for the Angel Art.

Christine for nagging me to finish this.
(Some people do need it, you are right)

Paul for being my best friend.
(I can do that because it's my book and you
should never forget your best friend!)

Last but certainly not least, **Jane** for your patience,
love and support while writing this. X

MEET THE PRODUCTION TEAM

–

Author
Ged Thompson
www.angeluspoetry.com

–

Illustrations
Elizabeth Jones
www.elfinbow.com

–

Design & Typography
Thomas Woollam
thomaswoollam@live.co.uk

–

Photography
Elle Buetow
elle@ellephoto.ca

–

Printed by
Lonsdale Direct
www.lonsdaledirect.co.uk

ABOUT THE AUTHOR

Ged Thompson is a Liverpool-
born performance poet, writer and
storyteller who some would say
"never quite got the hang of being
a grown up". He is very pleased to
present to you his debut collection
of fairytales for children and adults
that didn't quite get the hang
of it either.

ELFIN BOW

Elfin Bow believes in the power of creativity to connect, heal, dream and grow. Inspired by both the vastness and intricacies of nature, art has always been her passion and from a young age, she has sought opportunities to pursue her dreams of a creative life.

www.elfinbow.com

WORKSHOPS AVAILABLE

Ged is currently designing and
leading our educational poetry
workshop projects. These projects
aim to develop emotional and
cognitive development via writing
and performance based poetry/
storytelling. If you would like to
know more about the different ranges
of art based workshops we have
available please visit our website.

www.angeluspoetry.com

Thank you for buying this book...

St Vincent's is a residential school for visually impaired pupils aged four to nineteen. Our mission is to challenge high unemployment rates for visually impaired pupils upon leaving education (typically 85%) by introducing project based learning opportunities attached to their individual strengths and skill sets alongside entrepreneurial learning. Our thanks go to all who buy this book and the author, as Ged has gifted a percentage of book sales to the school for future projects, through which we can help pupils make their entrepreneurial ideas reality.

Dr. John A Patterson
Principal

For more information on St Vincent's please visit:
www.stvin.com
Twitter @StvincentsL12

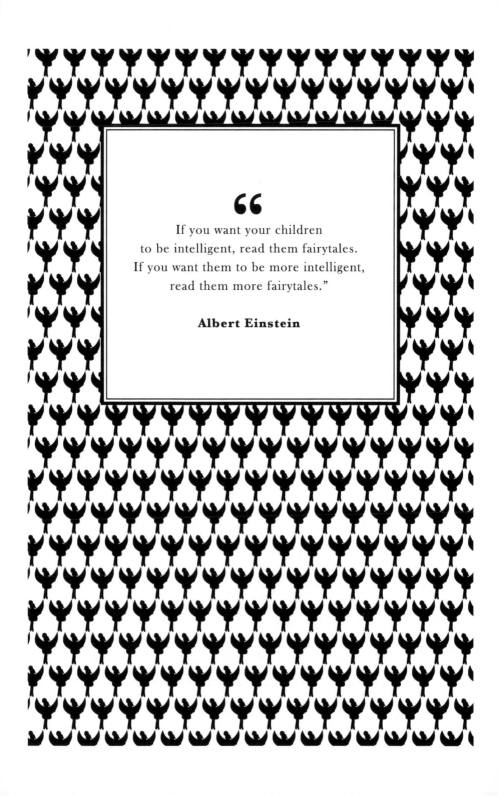

"

If you want your children
to be intelligent, read them fairytales.
If you want them to be more intelligent,
read them more fairytales."

Albert Einstein

① -40

3593
3433
3833
10859

2-28

2761
2957
3175
8893

3- 25

4239
2680
3963
10882

4-27

2107
2965
3889
8961

5-28

2691
3131
2937
8759

⑥ ㉚

3233
3816
3554

⑦ 36

1850
1946
3105

8-25

2847
2875
3330

⑨-20

3252
3541
2097